This book belongs to:

....

....

....

An Hachette UK Company
www.hachette.co.uk

First published in France in 2013 by Dessain et Tolra

This edition published in Great Britain in 2015 by
Hamlyn, a division of Octopus Publishing Group Ltd
Carmelite House
50 Victoria Embankment
London EC4Y oDZ
www.octopusbooksusa.com

Distributed in the US by
Hachette Book Group
1290 Avenue of the Americas
4th and 5th Floors
New York, NY 10020

Distributed in Canada by
Canadian Manda Group
664 Annette St.
Toronto, Ontario, Canada M6S 2C8

ISBN 978-0-600-63260-3

Printed and bound in China

10 9 8 7 6 5 4 3 2

Editorial directors: Isabelle Jeuge-Maynart and Ghislaine Stora
Layout and cover: Claire Morel Fatio
Translation: JMS Books LLP (www.jmswords.com)
Assistant Production Manager: Caroline Alberti

Coloring for mindfulness

GARDEN

*50 designs to
help you de-stress*

hamlyn

Forget everyday cares and worries!

Be transported back to the simple joys of childhood as you color in these pretty designs. Do you remember how much pleasure coloring in gave you and how peaceful you would feel? Or if you've ever doodled in the margins of notes or colored in images in a magazine while chatting on the phone, you'll know it's fun and doesn't require any particular skill. It's a link to the child that you once were and gives you the chance for a quiet pause in the day. And finally, it reawakens the creativity that is in all of us.

When you are feeling stressed, there's nothing like losing yourself in choosing colors and carefully filling in some figurative or abstract shapes. The blank designs are a great way to reboot a brain too occupied with the demands of smartphones and tablets.

In this book you will find 50 designs inspired by nature. Just choose one that appeals to you instinctively, at random, and begin. There are no rules: use whatever medium you like—felt tips, pencils, gouache, pastels —and whatever colors you like from the selection available. You will gradually feel calmer and soon be completely absorbed in what you are doing and the colors filling up the shapes. Concentrate on the smallest details.

There are also some blank spaces to fill with your own shapes and designs, while some designs have been begun with dotted lines and it's up to you to complete them, guided by just your imagination and chance. Finally, to help with concentration and meditation, cut out the designs that inspire you the most and contemplate them in a calm environment, allowing your thoughts to roam free.

Just 5 to 10 minutes of coloring a day will help you to relax and find inner peace.

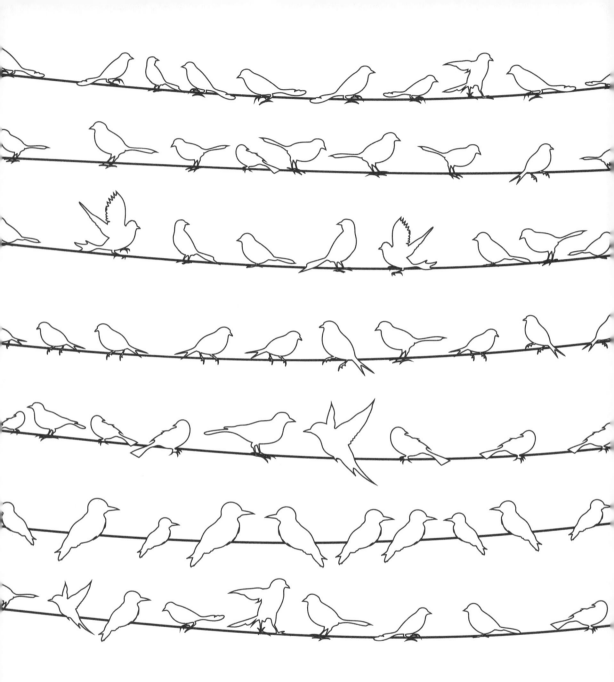

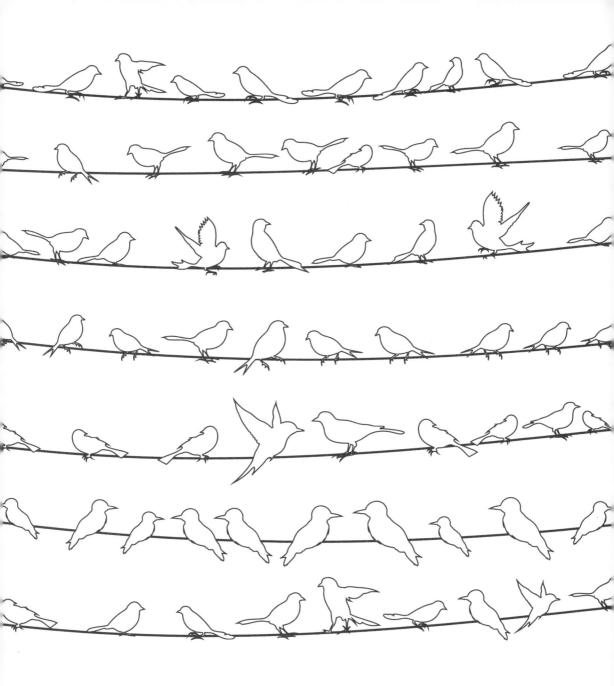

Add more branches and leaves, however you wish...

Give your imagination free rein and complete the design

Draw along the dotted lines and complete the
design with shapes inspired by nature

Draw along the dotted lines and complete the design
with different kinds of flower and leaf shapes

Complete and color in this design in whatever way you wish

Complete this design with a network of stems and leaves

Fill in the pond with imaginary fish

Add some butterflies and dragonflies

Fill in or surround the design with different motifs

Add some birds and their
fledglings to the branches

Add some more flower-filled
branches and flying birds

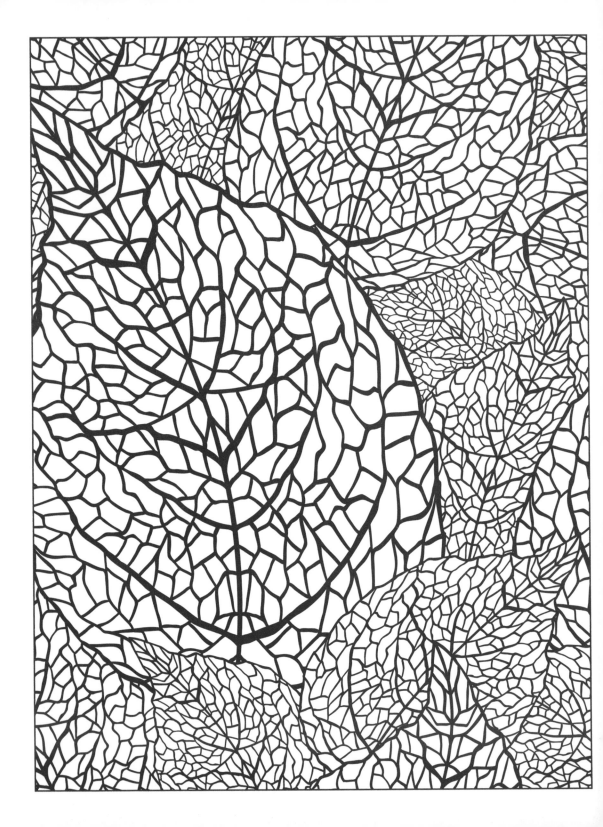